MW00610189

This book belongs to:

Copyright © 2021 by SINA CARROLL-BROWN
Printed in the United States of America

All rights reserved. This book or portions thereof may not be reproduced or transmitted in any form or by any means -- electronic, mechanical, photocopying, recording, or otherwise without the prior written permission of the authors.
ISBN: 978-0-578-87988-8

Illustrations by Reginald Byers

THE BIG DAY

By Sina Carroll-Brown

Illustrated by Reggie Byers

Dedication

To all my foster babies, thank you
for all the happiness and joy you
all have brought into my life.
I know that you don't remember
the time spent in my home with
us, but just know that each and
every one of you have taught
me different lessons and a ton
of patience.
Always know that mommy Sina
loves and misses all of u.

Hi!

My name is Ianiyah and this is my mommy and daddy.

I am a five year-old kindergartener.

My favorite color is pink, and I love to color and play outdoors.

Mommy says that today is a
BIG DAY!
We are going to a big building
to officially become a real family.
My mommy is not my
"tummy mommy".
She is my "everyday" mommy
and I have an "everyday" daddy too.

My "tummy mommy" was not able to take care of me, so I went into foster care.

Foster care is when another family cares for you when your mommy and daddy cannot.

I was very scared at first,
but my "everyday" mommy and
daddy were very nice to me.
They hugged me whenever I was
sad and even when I cried.

I miss my "tummy mommy"
very much.

She is in heaven watching over me.

I now have a bonus family with two grandmas and two pop pops.

Today, mommy and daddy says that a man wearing a black cape, called a judge, will bang his gavel and announce that we are a family.

I am so excited.

We arrived at the courthouse
wearing matching t-shirts
to celebrate this special day.

As we walked into the big room,
I saw my grandmas, pop pops,
and my uncle.

Everyone was very happy.

The judge asked my mommy and daddy if they would take care of me from now on.

Mommy started crying but she said she was very happy.

Mommy told me that she couldn't have any babies in her tummy.

She and daddy prayed to God for me and now they have me. The judge then announced that we are now an official family.

I looked around at everyone crying.

I was given lots of hugs and kisses from my mommy and daddy.

After we left the judge, we went to celebrate. I played games and ate lots of pizza.

It was the best day ever and so much fun.

Mommy and daddy said, "We get to start a new beginning."

WE ARE A FAMILY!

THANK YOU!

Made in the USA
Middletown, DE
05 April 2021

36642770R10015